COLOR MY OWN
DANCE
STORY

AN IMMERSIVE, CUSTOMIZABLE COLORING BOOK FOR KIDS
(THAT RHYMES!)

BRIAN C HAILES

For information about permission to reproduce selections from this book, please write Permissions, Epic Edge Publishing, 1934 Fielding Hill Ln, Draper, UT 84020.

www.epicedgepublishing.com

Library of Congress Cataloging-in-Publication Data
Color My Own Dance Story: An Immersive, Customizable Coloring Book for Kids (That Rhymes!)
Written by Brian C Hailes

p. cm.

Summary: The call sheet is up for all you beautiful little dancers to twirl your way through the pages of your very own coloring book, fill-in-the-blank activity and rhyming storybook—all in one! This vibrant, inspiring coloring story is perfect for darling dancers and aspiring artists alike!

Every budding ballerina that's prepared for a performance will love using their sheer creativity and hard work ethic to color, rhyme and become the hero or heroine of their own fantastic dancing tale. Full of dancers and fabulous scenes, this storybook is packed with ballerinas, pointy ballet shoes, sparkly tiaras, tutus, stage curtains and much more! Little girls and dancers everywhere will have a blast as they let their imaginations leap off the page! Splash your own vibrant colors onto each spread and take center stage to create your own stunning masterpieces.

As always, the dance must go on . . . and you are the dancer here. So take your place, and let's color and rhyme this fairytale together!

(Intended for children ages 6-12 . . . or all kids at heart)

1. Childrens—Dance. 2. Childrens—Coloring
3. Childrens—Performance
II. Hailes, Brian C., ill. III. Title.

Paperback ISBN-13: 978-1-951374-55-6
Hardback ISBN-13: 978-1-951374-56-3

Printed in the USA
Designed by Epic Edge Publishing

10 9 8 7 6 5 4 3 2 1

"Dance is visual poetry that celebrates the human form, the human condition, its divinity, origin and promise."

— *B.C. Hailes*

COLOR MY OWN
DANCE
STORY

AN IMMERSIVE, CUSTOMIZABLE COLORING BOOK FOR KIDS
(THAT RHYMES!)

STARRING: _____
(your name)

The music plays, the audience waits,

I take my place behind the curtain;

Into position, _____ shoes tight,
(dance, toe or jazz)

Practiced steps in my head ring certain . . .

It's all about the dance, the floating,

Gliding through the air!

The action and the lines,

_____'s _____ with a flair!

(Your dance of choice)   (beauty, power or grandeur)

Whether ballroom, ballet, hip hop or jazz,

The body's movement is the answer;

My name is _____ ,
(your full name)

And I choose to live life, I'm a dancer!

With all the wardrobe, glitz, accessories,

I become a brand new me;

A powerhouse, an angel, one that's

_____ and free!

(Elegant, Capable or Expressive)

I'm only _____ feet tall,
(your height)

But I can move with style and grace;

I can jump and step and bounce and turn,

And always find my place.

Confidence is the name of the game,

Even when you don't know what you're doing!

To _____ it is a talent, and
(hide, mask or veil)

It's one that's worth pursuing!

Culture also plays an important part

Of who I really am!

I was born in _____ ,
(where you are from)

And _____ music's my favorite jam!
(your favorite type of music)

I like to get all dressed up,

And then _____ about the room,
(spin, reel or twirl)

Moving to the rhythm, like a

Joyful, sweeping broom!

Or simply curtsy or bow, taking

My _____ by the hand,
(partner, friend or date)

And, becoming one, finding

Synchronization with the band.

Dance can be fun or serious,

Elegant, smooth or rough;

No matter your style, you've gotta have

_____ , and you've also gotta be tough!

(Form, A plan or Poise)

One must feel the music, whether

Loud, soft or in your head;

One can't discount the rhythm, the _____,
(rhyme, flow or beat)

Or with unsteadiness, you'll tread.

With eyes of _____ ,
(your eye color)

And _____ , _____ hair,
(long or short)   (your hair color)

I am unique, and so well-practiced,

But I require no big fanfare.

To merely dance is _____ enough,
(reward, award or praise)

I do it for the joy;

For this is what I am, and my

Very best effort, I'll employ!

Τo learn the _____ , I find a challenge;
(steps, dance or routine)

Things worth doing can be hard!

Clumsy mistakes, missteps, off-timing

Serve to keep me on my guard!

But in the end, I will _____ ;

(prevail, triumph or succeed)

I will master every dance;

It will become natural, fluid, fluent, and

I'll share it at every chance!

True dancers are the rarest _____,

(gift, breed or treasure)

And an absolute joy to behold;

So I'll spend the time and practice,

Unafraid of being bold.

Polished, hardwood floors, _____ ,
(concrete, carpet, or vinyl)

Or a glistening sheet of ice

Can carry me to speedy heights

And, of Heaven, offer me a slice!

Ice skating, _____ , hula or tap,
(drill team, samba or modern)

All dance is a gift from above;

Expressions of joy from all angles and walks,

All creative expressions of love!

Contemporary, folk, Irish or swing,

There are so many dance style choices;

The one that calls out to me, above all,

Is _____ ; it's the clearest of voices.
(your favorite dance)

But whatever your pleasure, let's do it together,

For more is always more fun!

Listen close to the melody, rhythm and beat;

What more can the _____ become?

(cadence, tune, notes,
or tempo)

Ballerinas, pasos, jitterbugs,

As well as those engaged in waltz;

It's all about your strengths and _____ ,

(verve, clout or nerve)

And not about your faults!

So put your _____ to focused work,
(feet, body or spirit)
And never give up on the chance;

To everything there is a season,

And always a time to dance!

THE END

OTHER "COLOR MY OWN" TITLES NOW AVAILABLE!

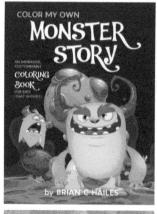

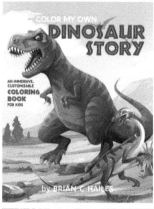
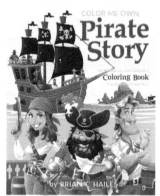

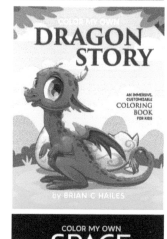

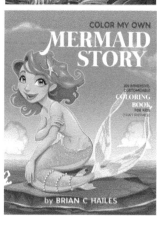

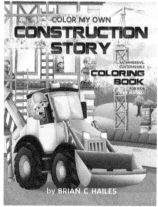

ABOUT THE AUTHOR

BRIAN C HAILES, creator of Draw It With Me (www.drawitwithme.com), is also the award-winning writer/illustrator of over forty-five (and counting) novels, children's picture books, comics and graphic novels, including Blink: An Illustrated Spy Thriller Novel, Devil's Triangle, Dragon's Gait, Skeleton Play, Don't Go Near the Crocodile Ponds, If I Were a Spaceman, Here, There Be Monsters, Heroic, Passion & Spirit, Continuum (Arcana Studios), as well as McKenna, McKenna, Ready to Fly, and Grace & Sylvie: A Recipe for Family (American Girl), among others. In addition to his publishing credits, Hailes has also illustrated an extensive collection of fantasy, science fiction, and children's book covers as well as interior magazine illustrations. Hailes has received numerous awards for his works from across the country, including Winner of the L. Ron Hubbard Illustrators of the Future contest out of Hollywood. His artwork has also been featured in the 2017-2020 editions of Infected By Art.

Hailes studied illustration and graphic design at Utah State University where he received his Bachelor of Fine Arts degree, as well as the Academy of Art University in San Francisco.

He currently lives in Salt Lake City with his wife and four boys, where he continues to write, paint and draw regularly. More of his work can be seen at HailesArt.com

Other Titles Available from
Epic Edge Publishing

Illustrated Novels	Graphic Novels / Comics	Childrens Picture Books	Anthologies	Non-Fiction

Blink: An Illustrated Spy Thriller Novel
by Brian C Hailes

Avila
(Available 2021!)
by Robert J Defendi
& Brian C Hailes

Devil's Triangle: The Complete Graphic Novel
by Brian C Hailes
& Blake Casselman

Dragon's Gait
by Brian C Hailes

KamiKazi
by John English
& Brian C Hailes

If I Were a Spaceman: A Rhyming Adventure Through the Cosmos
by Brian C Hailes
& Tithi Luadthong

Here, There Be Monsters
by Brian C Hailes
& Tithi Luadthong

Don't Go Near the Crocodile Ponds
by Brian C Hailes

Skeleton Play
by Brian C Hailes

Can We Be Friends?
by Edie New
& Cindy Hailes

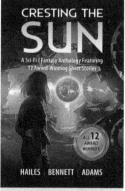

Cresting the Sun: A Sci-fi / Fantasy Anthology Featuring 12 Award-Winning Short Stories
by Brian C Hailes,
Rick Bennett
& Nicholas Adams

Heroic: Tales of the Extraordinary
by Blake Casselman,
David Farland,
Michael Stackpole
& more

Draw It With Me: The Dynamic Female Figure
(Available 2020!)
by Brian C Hailes

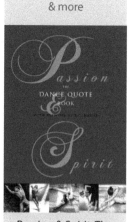

DIWM 2020 Annual 1
(Available 2020!)
by Brian C Hailes,
Heather Edwards
& more

Passion & Spirit: The Dance Quote Book
by Brian C Hailes

9 781951 374563